D1588890

This edition of *My Little Christening Book* published in Great Britain in 2017

Society for Promoting Christian Knowledge
36 Causton Street, London SW1P 4ST
www.spck.org.uk

Copyright © Anno Domini Publishing 2017
www.ad-publishing.com
Text copyright © Anno Domini Publishing: Sally Ann Wright 2017
Illustrations copyright © Frank Endersby 2017

All rights reserved. No part of this book may be reproduced or transmitted in any
form or by any means, electronic or mechanical, including photocopying, recording,
or by any information storage and retrieval system, without permission in writing
from the publisher.

SPCK does not necessarily endorse the individual views contained in its publications.

British Library Cataloguing-in-Publication Data
A catalogue record for this book is available from the British Library
Gift case ISBN 978—0—281—07697—0
NOT FOR INDIVIDUAL SALE
Printed and bound in China

My Little Christening Book

Sally Ann Wright
and Frank Endersby

Here I am!

'It is in the home that children experience their first relationship of love…

Just as all of us receive the gifts of loving because God first loved us, so children receive the capacity to love through their experience of their parents.'

Jack Dominian

My name is..

I was born on this date..

I was born at this time ....

I was born at this address...

....

....

....

I weighed this much...

My hair was..

My eyes were...

Lord, you know me and you love me.
Thank you for watching me grow in my mother's womb.
Thank you that I am special to you.
From Psalm 139

My first visitors

Children are a blessing and a
gift from the Lord.
Psalm 127:3

The people who came to see me...

....

....

....

....

....

....

....

....

Thank you, Father God,
for the safe delivery of this new baby,
for the miracle of new life,
for the wonder of a new creation,
and for the mystery of human love.
Thank you that you know our names
and you have loved us
from the very beginning.
Be near us as we learn
the joys and challenges of being parents,
and help us to trust you to provide
for all our needs.

This is my family

Name ....

Date and place of birth...

....

Name ....

Date and place of birth...

....

Name ....

Date and place of birth...

....

Name ....

Date and place of birth...

....

Name ....

Date and place of birth ....

....

....

Thank you, God, for my parents, for brothers and sisters,
aunties and uncles and cousins.
Thank you for the gift of my family.
Thank you that you are here with us,
that your love surrounds us,
and that you have given us each other to care for,
learn from and share with, day by day.

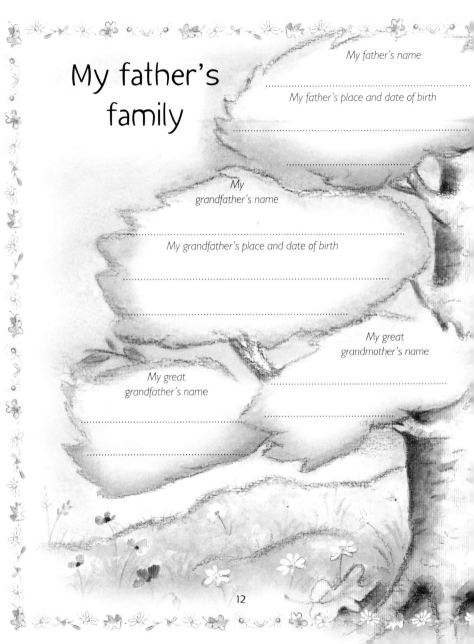

My father's family

My father's name

....

My father's place and date of birth

....

....

My grandfather's name

....

My grandfather's place and date of birth

....

....

My great grandmother's name

....

My great grandfather's name

....

....

My grandmother's name

....

My grandmother's place and date of birth

....

....

My great
grandfather's name

My great
grandmother's name

....

....

My mother's family

My mother's name

....

My mother's place and date of birth

....

....

My grandfather's name

....

My grandfather's place and date of birth

....

....

My great grandmother's name

....

My great grandfather's name

....

....

My grandmother's name

....

My grandmother's place and date of birth

....

....

My great
grandfather's name

....

....

My great
grandmother's name

....

....

My grandparents

Father God,
Thank you for giving us families to care for us.
Thank you for those who have been anxious
as we have been anxious;
for those who have been strong when problems arise.
Thank you for their wisdom and courage and strength.
Help us to learn from those who have gone before us
And love them as they love us.

Things my grandparents wish for me

....

....

....

....

....

Things my grandparents want me to know about them

....

....

....

....

....

....

My home

My home address ....

....

....

Where I sleep ....

....

....

Lord Jesus, you shared in Nazareth the life of an earthly home.
Bless our home now with peace and joy.
Give to parents strength and wisdom as the sun rises each morning,
Love and patience to get through each day,
and peaceful rest as the stars light up the night sky.

Lord God, you made the world and it was very good.
Lord God, you gave me a home,
a place where I can be safe from harm.
Lord God, you gave me people to love me and care for me.
Thank you for all the good things you have given me.

My progress

'Teach a child how
he should live
and he will remember
it all his life.'
Proverbs 22:6

Date of my first smile ....

Date of my first tooth ....

I first slept through the night on ....

Lord, bless us and protect us.
Lord, smile on us and show us your love
Take care of us and help us.
Amen

I first sat up unaided on ....

I first crawled on ....

I first spoke on ....

My first words were ....

I first stood alone on ....

I took my first steps on ....

My first immunisation ....

My first illnes s ....

My first dry night ....

My first ....

Jesus, Friend of little children,
be a friend to me;
take my hand, and ever keep me
close to thee.
Walter J. Matham (1853-1931)

21

My special things

My pets ....

My best friends ....

My favourite toys ....

My favourite story ....

My favourite game ....

My favourite sound ....

My favourite colour ....

My favourite foods ....

My favourite drinks ....

Things I like to d o..

....

....

....

....

Dear God,
Thank you for my friends.
Thank you for my toys and special things.
Please teach me to share all I have with others.
Amen

Thank you for the world so sweet,
Thank you for the food we eat,
Thank you for the birds that sing,
Thank you God for everything.

23

My baptismal day

Thank you, Heavenly Father,
for the child you have given us to care for.
Help us to be loving and patient,
always quick to support and to forgive.
Guide us in all we do so that our love may show your love,
and the blessing given today may be with him every day,
keeping him safe from harm,
and helping him to grow up to find purpose
in loving and serving you.

Date of baptism ....

Place of baptism ....

....

Age at baptism ....

Names of godparents or sponsors ....

....

Family who attended the service ....

....

....

....

Friends who attended the service ....

....

....

....

Jesus said,
'Let the little children come to me.
Don't stop them!
For the Kingdom of Heaven belongs
to those who are like these children.'
And he placed his hands on their heads
and blessed them.

Matthew 19:14-15

Special times

'Each day comes just
once in a lifetime –
today you are creating
tomorrow's memories.
Invest in positive memories
for childhood memories shape
the person of the future.'
Marion Stroud

My first Christmas

I spent my first Christmas at ....

My age was ....

I shared my first Christmas with ....

....

....

On my first Christmas I ate ....

....

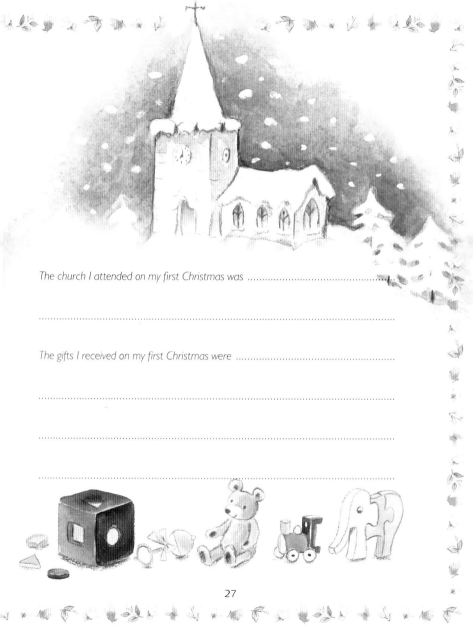

The church I attended on my first Christmas was ....

....

The gifts I received on my first Christmas were ....

....

....

....

My first holiday

May the road rise to meet you.
May the wind be always at your back.
May the sunshine warm upon your face.
May the rains fall softly upon your fields.
Until we meet again,
May God hold you in the hollow of his hand.

An Irish Blessing

Where I spent my first holiday ....

....

My age was ....

Special places I saw and visited ....

....

The people I shared my first holiday with ....

....

Things I did on my first holiday ....

....

....

Lord God, who never slumbers or sleeps,
bless us as we travel
and keep us safe as we return,
now and always.
Based on Psalm 121